MW00620369

# Circle Your World with Prayer

## John Hendrix & Ann B. Cannon

LifeWay Press
Nashville, Tennessee

This book is based upon *Circle Your World with Prayer Retreat Booklet*
© Copyright 1985 The Sunday School Board of the Southern Baptist
Convention.

ISBN 0-7673-9355-4

This book is the text for course number CG-0492 in the subject area
"Prayer" in the Christian Growth Category of the Christian Growth
Study Plan.

Dewey Decimal Classification Number: 248.32
Subject Heading: PRAYER\YOUTH-RELIGIOUS LIFE

Unless indicated otherwise, all Scripture quotations are from the Holy
Bible, *New International Version,* copyright © 1973, 1978, 1984 by
International Bible Society.

Printed in the United States of America
To order additional copies of this resource: WRITE LifeWay Church
Resources Customer Service, 127 Ninth Avenue, North, Nashville, TN
37234-0113; FAX order to (615) 251-5933; PHONE 1-800-458-2772;
EMAIL to CustomerService@lifeway.com; ONLINE at www.lifeway.com;
or visit the LifeWay Christian Store serving you.

Youth Section
Discipleship and Family Group
LifeWay Christian Resources
of the Southern Baptist Convention
127 Ninth Avenue, North
Nashville, TN  37234-0152

# Table of Contents

## THE WRITERS

**John D. Hendrix** is pastor of Northside Baptist Church in Clinton, Mississippi. Previously he was the Basil Manly, Jr. Professor of Christian Education at The Southern Baptist Theological Seminary, Louisville, Kentucky. A Missouri native, John is a graduate of William Jewell College and Midwestern and New Orleans Baptist Theological Seminaries.

**Ann B. Cannon** writes extensively for students, parents of students, and those who work with both. She also travels as a consultant in various areas of student work. She and her husband, Cecil, have been blessed many times by the circle of friends who pray for them. She thanks God daily for the pleasure of prayer.

## INTRODUCTION

- Do I have to be a Christian to pray?
- Why pray if God already knows my needs?
- How can I pray when I don't feel God's presence?
- Why should I pray for others when I have enough troubles of my own?
- Why doesn't God answer my prayers like I want Him too?
- Why should I pray when I know God's not going to change this horrible situation I'm stuck in?
- How can God hear my prayer when so many others are praying?

Do you have questions like that? Then, you can learn something about prayer. The first 13 chapters of the Book of Acts form the foundation for this study. The early Christians were a praying people. As you explore their circle, focus on how their experiences relate to you today.

# Prayer
# Centered in Jesus

## Session 1

To understand The Acts of the Apostles—also known as the New Testament Book of Acts— you need to remember why Acts was recorded. If it hadn't been for Jesus, there would be no apostles, no Christian church, and no mission trips to tell others about Him. Jesus is the reason there is an Acts. Remember how Jesus.... Wait a minute.... You know this story, right?

**Put the following events in the life of Jesus in chronological order by numbering the events from 1 (first) to 10 (last).**
_____ **died on a cross as King of the Jews**
_____ **ascended into heaven to be with God**
_____ **traveled three years with a band of disciples**
_____ **born in Bethlehem under unusual circumstances**
_____ **mysteriously raised from death after three days**
_____ **accused by religious Jews of blasphemy; they said He claimed to be God's Son**
_____ **grew up in Nazareth as the son of Mary and Joseph**
_____ **taught His followers to pray by giving an example**
_____ **buried in a borrowed tomb**
_____ **seen by 500 people after the resurrection**
_(Check your answers by surfing through Matthew, Mark, or Luke.)_

## WHAT DOES JESUS HAVE TO DO WITH PRAYER?
• Jesus prayed on earth. If Jesus was God, why did He pray?
• Jesus told His disciples to pray in His name _(John 14:13)_. If prayer is talking to God, shouldn't you say "In my name I pray, Amen"?

- Jesus is the reason we can pray to God *(Heb. 2:17)*. What's a high priest got to do with Jesus and prayer?
- Jesus is alive. If Jesus lives in Christians through the Holy Spirit, why don't all Christians act the way Jesus did when He lived on earth?
- Jesus is with us now *(Matt. 18:20)*. Does someone have to be with you to make prayer work? Why or why not?

**Circle your response to each of the following statements about prayer. Be prepared to support your answer.**

| | | |
|---|---|---|
| **Agree** | **Disagree** | **1. An important key to vital prayer is knowing that Jesus is alive.** |
| **Agree** | **Disagree** | **2. Jesus speaks to you only through prayer.** |
| **Agree** | **Disagree** | **3. God guarantees answers to your prayers through Jesus.** |
| **Agree** | **Disagree** | **4. Don't pray if you don't have a reason to talk to God.** |
| **Agree** | **Disagree** | **5. Before Jesus came, people couldn't pray.** |

After Jesus left earth, God sent a new presence that empowered the disciples and followers of Jesus. With this power—the Holy Spirit—these people established a Christian community built on faith in Jesus Christ. The Roman world, where these Christians lived, would never be the same again once the early Christian community began its work. How did they make such a difference in their world? Easy. The early Christians changed their world through prayer. The Book of Acts tells how the people prayed and how God responded.

## WHAT'S PRAYER ALL ABOUT?

**Complete the sentence, Prayer is . . .**
❑ **talking to God.**
❑ **listening to God.**
❑ **connecting with God spiritually.**
❑ **informing God of what He already knows we need.**
❑ **a way of showing obedience and love to God.**
❑ **a way of learning obedience and love from God.**

Actually, all of these define different parts of prayer. Look up the following passages in Acts. Identify the person who prayed. Then using the six definitions of prayer on the bottom of page 6 select a definition that best describes what kind of prayer was occurring in each Scripture passage.

| Scripture | Who Prayed | Definition |
|---|---|---|
| Acts 2:42 | | |
| Acts 6:3-6 | | |
| Acts 7:59-60 | | |
| Acts 9:10-11 | | |
| Acts 9:40 | | |
| Acts 10:9-13 | | |
| Acts 12:5 | | |
| Acts 13:3 | | |

**From your study, how would you define prayer? Write your definition here:** _____

_____

_____

_____

_____

_____

## THE WEEK THAT WAS

On the calendar on the next page rate each day of this past week using the descriptions provided. Under each day mark a dot representing how you felt. For example, if you had lots of tests on Monday, your mom screamed at you, and a friend scratched your favorite CD, you might put a dot under Monday beside "trashed." Put a dot somewhere for each day.

| | Sun | Mon | Tues | Wed | Thurs | Fri | Sat |
|---|---|---|---|---|---|---|---|

totally
incredible

super

OK

tolerable

bad
day

barely
hanging on

trashed

When you have marked something for each day connect the dots. Now, mark a small cross (+) under each day across from the phrase that expresses your prayer life for this week. For example, if you enjoyed a meaningful time alone with God on Thursday, put a cross under Thursday on the line next to "super." When you have marked something for each day connect the crosses.

**What connections do you see between the bad experiences of this past week and your attention to prayer for that day?**

_____

_____

**On those difficult days did you pray? Why or why not?** _____

_____

_____

**If you pray every day are you going to have good days? Why or why not?** _____

_____

_____

**Think about the priority you put on Jesus this past week, and the part prayer played. Circle the words that best summarize this past week for you.**

| | |
|---|---|
| exciting | boring |
| sad | unorganized |
| surprising | disappointing |
| difficult | good |
| lonely | stressful |
| peaceful | humiliating |
| miserable | adventurous |
| encouraging | ridiculous |
| painful | tiring |

## THE CENTER OF PRAYER

- How important is a center to the offense in football?
- How does a center help a basketball team?
- What is the center of gravity?
- Why do CDs have a center?
- What would happen if the bull's-eye was missing from a target?

Centers are important. Centers make a difference. Prayer centered in Jesus makes a difference. In this session you've seen how important Jesus is to prayer.
- Jesus taught us to pray.
- Jesus prays to God for us.
- The authority of Jesus' name allows God to listen to our prayers.
- We can talk to Jesus in prayer any time.

**Read _Acts 2:36_ in your Bible. This verse comes at the end of Peter's first sermon (it must have been pretty good, because about 3000 folks were baptized that day)! Peter called Jesus Lord and Christ.**

**Lord**—A lord was the owner, the chief person who ran the ranch. Jesus as Lord was the main man who represented God on earth. Jesus had the power and the authority of His Father. The early Christians confessed "Jesus is Lord" to acknowledge Jesus' power over life and death. They would say this phrase to one another as a reminder and as a way of identifying themselves to other Christians.

**Christ**—In ancient Hebrew language Christ meant the "anointed one." People were anointed for a special position, either to become a priest, a ruler, or a person in a high office. For the Jews living in the time of Acts, Christ meant "Messiah"—the long-expected king who would rescue the Jewish people from the Romans. Even though God promised a Messiah, many who actually encountered Jesus didn't believe Him when He talked about being the Messiah.

**Think about it for a minute. What are your thoughts on Jesus being Lord and Christ the Messiah?** _____

_____

_____

_____

_____

## PRAYER CIRCLE

Can you see it? It's important to understand these concepts. Maybe a visual will help. Let's illustrate prayer and the truth that Jesus is Lord and Christ by using a circle. You will add to this drawing each session.

**In the center of the circle write: The Center, Lord Jesus Christ, Acts 2:36.**

## REFLECT

• **What do you want to remember about this session?** _____

_____

_____

_____

• **How does knowing Jesus is the center of your prayer life make you feel? Pick a word and explain why you chose it.**

❑ **Confident**_____

❑ **Confused** _____

❑ **Cared for** _____

## REACT

**During these studies you will have an opportunity to pray. You can begin now. Complete these sentences:**

• **A person I want to pray for is (you can use initials if you prefer) . . .**

_____

• **A prayer concern I have in my life is . . .** _____

_____

_____

• **My prayer for this study time is . . .** _____

_____

_____

• **The main question I still have about prayer is . . .** _____

_____

_____

## REQUEST

**Dear God,**
**Right now I feel** _____. **I would like to feel**
_____. **I come to you requesting help for (name or initials)**
_____. **A major concern I have in my life is**
_____. **I pray that you will work through**
**me to** _____. **Thank you for**
_____.

**In Jesus' name I pray,**
**Amen.**

# Asking
## The Power of Prayer

Anything You Want.
Just Ask .
It's Yours Free,
No Strings Attached,
I Promise!

- **If you read these words in a magazine or heard them on TV or radio, would you believe them? Why or why not?** _____
  _____
  _____

- **Would the promise be more believable if your favorite movie star, your pastor, or your best friend said it?** _____
  _____
  _____

When is a promise not a promise? When you don't trust the person making the promise. If you believe this person and know he keeps his promises, then the value of the promise goes up. If the person making the promise is someone you don't know, someone you don't trust, or someone who breaks promises, then the promise is worthless, no matter how terrific it sounds.

- **What promises have you made in the last few weeks?** _____
  _____
  _____
  _____

• **Were you able to keep your promises? Why or why not?** _____

_____

_____

• **What was the most significant promise someone made to you?**

_____

_____

• **What broken promise hurt you the most? What were the results of that broken promise?** _____

_____

_____

## THE PROMISE

On His last day on earth Jesus made a promise. In *Acts 1:4* Jesus promised that a gift was on the way. The gift was from His Father.

**Read *Acts 2:1–4*. The promise was the gift of the** __ __ __ __ __
__ __ __ __ __ **(two words).**

Two symbols illustrated this gift. The symbol of sound—a violent wind; and a symbol of sight—tongues of fire. Both symbolized the power of the Holy Spirit, the presence and power of God living in believers.

_____ **If I had been in the room during this event, the sound of the violent wind would leave me feeling ❑ fearful; ❑ excited; ❑ confused; ❑ inspired. I chose this emotion because** _____.

_____ **If I had been in the room during this event, the sight of tongues of fire would make me ❑ run away; ❑ call 911; ❑ forget what to do in case of fire; ❑ want the power; ❑ watch in awe. I chose this action because** _____
_____.

**Read *Acts 1:14*. What were the people doing when the Holy Spirit came?** _____

## THE POWER OF PRAYER

When the people prayed, things happened. The coming of the Holy Spirit cranked up the witnessing movement that told the world about the life, death, and resurrection of Jesus Christ. Peter demonstrated the effectiveness of Jesus' promise of the Holy Spirit.

**Read *Matthew 26:69-75*. Using Peter's name as an acrostic, write down four words that describe Peter on the night before Jesus died. An example is given.**

**P**

**E**

**T**

**t E a r f u l**

**R**

**Compare Peter on that night to the Peter who spoke to the people in Jerusalem after he received the Holy Spirit. Read *Acts 2:14,29-41*. Describe Peter using "power" as the acrostic.**

**P**

**O**

**W**

**E**

**R**

## A PERSONAL PROMISE FOR YOU

Do you want to know how you can get that power? Read *Acts 2:38-39* again. If you have not accepted Jesus Christ as your personal Savior, talk to your leader about how to make that decision. If you have accepted

Jesus into your heart and believe He is the Son of God, then you already have the power. If you don't "feel" God's power, talk to your leader about how the Holy Spirit works in a believer's life.

## ASKING IN PRAYER

Some people think that prayer is asking God for lots of stuff. Asking is only one part of praying. Prayer involves other areas. Here's an acronym that reminds us of the four parts of prayer. The acronym also spells the name of the book of the Bible we are studying.

**A**doration      Praise God for who He is.
**C**onfession      Admit your sins to God and ask His forgiveness.
**T**hanksgiving      Thank God for all He has done.
**S**upplication      Ask for God's help.

When the people who believed in Jesus Christ asked in prayer, powerful things happened. People accepted Jesus as their Savior. Jesus' disciples turned from a confused band of timid men and women into a witnessing army. Unusual opportunities to share the story of Jesus occurred.

## ASKING FOR THE RIGHT THING

**Read *Acts 8:26-39* and answer these questions.**
**• Who were the people involved?**_____

_____

**• Why did the Ethiopian go to Jerusalem?**_____

_____

**• What basic message did Philip share with the man?**_____

_____

_____

**• What did the Ethiopian desire?**_____

_____

**• What were the results of his asking?**_____

_____

• **How do you think prayer was involved?** _____

_____

• **Why was the Ethiopian's request honored?** _____

_____

Philip was an evangelist in Samaria. The Ethiopian was a minister over the treasury in the court of Candace, queen of Ethiopia, a country located in eastern Africa. He went to Jerusalem to worship in the temple. On his way home, he met Philip. The Ethiopian was reading from the Book of Isaiah. It told about a prophet. He asked Philip about this prophet. Philip explained about Jesus. When the Ethiopian saw a pond, he made his decision and asked to be baptized.

• Though his country was pagan, the Ethiopian had heard about God.
• Jews did not associate with pagans. In order to share Jesus with the Ethiopian, Philip ignored the prejudices he had been taught.
• The Ethiopian was a eunuch. He couldn't be circumcised like Jewish men. This could have stopped Philip under other circumstances.
• Philip showed up at the right time, then disappeared.
• Though he didn't know Philip, the Ethiopian trusted his message.

## ASKING FOR THE WRONG THING
**Read *Acts 8:9-24* and answer these questions.**
• **Who were the people involved?**_____

• **What did Philip do for the man in this story?** _____

_____

• **What basic message did Philip share with the man?** _____

_____

• **Why was Samaria such a surprising place for a revival to occur?** _____

_____

• **How was prayer involved?** _____

_____

• **What did Simon want from the disciples?** _____

_____

• **What were the results of his asking?** _____

_____

• **Why was Simon's request refused?** _____

_____

This time Philip went into Samaria, a place the Jews avoided because the Samaritans and Jews didn't get along. But Philip ignored prejudices and led many Samaritans to accept Christ. Among those who believed in Jesus was Simon, the magician. Simon followed Philip everywhere.

The disciples traveled to Samaria to help Philip. Praying and laying hands on the people brought dramatic results. Simon offered to pay for the same power. But Peter made it clear that Simon's heart was not right and that he was praying for the wrong thing.

• **What can you learn from the Ethiopian and Simon?** _____

_____

_____

• **What can you ask God for?** _____

_____

• **What is a valid prayer request?** _____

_____

_____

• **Is any genuine prayer request too small? (For example, getting a date, making a good grade, winning a game, finding a lost item, asking for good weather, etc.)** _____

_____

_____

**On the left side of the circle on page 10 write: Asking, The Power of Prayer, Acts 4:31.**

## ASKING FOR OTHERS

Jesus told us to pray for one another. On His last night on earth Jesus prayed for His disciples, you, and me (*John 17:20-23*.) With the power of the Holy Spirit working in them, the disciples prayed for others.

**Look at the powerful, rocking results of Peter and John's prayer in *Acts 4:23-31*.**
• **Who did they pray for?** _____

_____

_____

• **What was the result?** _____

_____

_____

**Intercession is praying for others. Why pray for others? (Check all that apply.)**
❑ **They need all the prayer they can get.**
❑ **They don't know how to pray.**
❑ **They don't know they need Jesus.**
❑ **They are in a crisis.**
❑ **God works through you to reach others.**

**Where do you go regularly? List three of these places under "My World." Beside each place write the name or initials of a person who needs prayer. Then write a need. An example is provided.**

| My World | Person | Need |
|----------|--------|------|
| 1. home | my mom | problems at work |
| 2. | | |
| 3. | | |
| 4. | | |

## ASKING FOR YOURSELF

What do you really want from God? Try hard to recognize the difference between a valid prayer and an inappropriate request. What is your heart's desire? Pray your prayer of supplication (asking) right now.

## REFLECT

• **What do you want to remember about this session?**_____

_____

• **How do you feel knowing God expects you to ask in prayer?**_

_____

_____

• **What questions do you still have about asking God?**_____

_____

_____

## REACT

• **How can this study change your prayer life?**_____

_____

_____

• **Who are you praying for as an intercessor?**_____

_____

• **What are you asking God for in your life?**_____

_____

## REQUEST

**Dear God,**
**I've learned that supplication means I can ask, so I'm asking for**

_____.
**A part of my world that I am asking for help with is** _____.
**I'm also asking as an intercessor for** _____.
**In Jesus' holy name, I ask,**
**Amen.**

# Receiving
# The Profits of Prayer

**PRAYING FOR PROFIT**

• **Would you rather receive ❑ $100 each time you pray?
❑ have someone accept Christ each time you pray?**

• **Would you rather ❑ pray and receive a new car? ❑ pray and be cured of a fatal disease?**

• **Would you rather ❑ pray and receive a date for Friday night? ❑ pray and receive a high grade on a major test?**

• **Would you rather ❑ pray and receive the ability to end all world conflicts without recognition? ❑ pray and receive the applause and praise of others?**

• **Would you rather ❑ give? ❑ receive?**

Christians tend to pray for material things and forget the answers to prayers that last longer, like an ill person getting well or a person's salvation.

When Jesus gave you the power to pray in His name and with His authority, He wanted you to pray to God so that you would be blessed when God answered your prayers. The profits that come from praying are the gifts, blessings, joys, and answers you receive.

One way to respond is to thank God. That's the "T" part of ACTS. You've already studied the "S."

## SUPPLY THE MISSING LETTERS AND WORDS.

**A**doration        Praise God for who He is.

**C**onfession        Admit your sins to God and ask His forgiveness.

**T**hanksgiving        Thank God for all He has done.

**S** _____      Ask _____.

## PLENTY OF PROFITS

You can receive many benefits from praying to God. The profits, blessings, and benefits happen because you pray. Your spiritual side seeks the higher power of God. When you meet God in prayer, your first blessing comes from being in His presence. Other blessings occur as you pray. These may begin during your prayer and carry on through the day. Blessings come through answered prayers.

**Circle the profits, benefits, and blessings you have received through your prayers.**

| | |
|---|---|
| sense of peace | forgiveness for sin |
| comfort | salvation |
| protection | patience |
| feeling loved | guidance |
| confidence | feeling accepted |
| assurance | wisdom |
| personal relationship with God | encouragement |
| no fear | someone to listen |
| spiritual growth | reminder of God's creation |

**Other blessings:** _____.

## EXCUSE ME—DIDN'T YOU FORGET SOMETHING?

The subject of our story is a young girl named Rhoda. Her story can be found in *Acts 12:1-17*. Rhoda was so excited that her prayers were answered that she forgot to do a very important thing.

**The story on the following page has 13 mistakes. Read the story carefully and then identify the mistakes. Correct the mistakes by comparing this story to *Acts 12:1-17*. Circle the mistakes and record corrections.**

King Augustus arrested Christians, intending to feed them. He had James, the brother of John, killed by the sword. And, he arrested Paul on the Feast of Pentecost. The king put Paul in prison, having him guarded by four squads of four soldiers each. The rest of the Christians prayed to God for Paul's hunger.

The night before Paul was to stand trial, he was sleeping between two pillars, bound in chains, with guard dogs at the entrance to his cell. Suddenly an angel of the Lord appeared, a light flashed, and struck him blind. Then, the angel said, "Get up" and the chains fell off Paul's ankles.

Once Paul got dressed the angel led him passed the guards and out of prison. Paul thought he was dreaming. But when the angel disappeared Paul was free. He went to the house of Mary the mother of John Mark where he knew other pagans were praying. He rang the doorbell. A servant girl named Rhoda answered the door. When she heard Paul's voice, she got so excited she forgot to open the door, but ran back into the house to tell the others. So Paul climbed over the wall. Everyone was thrilled to see him since they had been praying for his release. They were amazed at the story he told about getting out of the kitchen.

- **Why was Rhoda surprised that God had answered their prayers for another Christian's freedom?** _____

_____

_____

_____

- **Have you ever been surprised by answered prayer? If so, how?**

_____

_____

_____

- **Do you expect God to answer your prayer every time? Why or why not?** _____

_____

_____

_____

• **When God has answered your prayer, why do you think He honored your request?** _____

_____

_____

• **Think about a time that you prayed for something you really wanted and your prayer was not answered the way you expected it to be. Why do you think God did not honor your request?**

_____

_____

✱

## PRAYING IN GOD'S WILL

When you pray "in God's will," your prayers will be answered. The tricky part is knowing how to recognize when it is God's will.

**Choose the definition that best defines God's will.**

_____ **1. The work God is doing in the world.**

_____ **2. The best thing for my life (but I still have choices).**

_____ **3. Something I'm to do, but don't always understand.**

_____ **4. A mysterious journey that I'm on as a Christian.**

_____ **5. A predetermined plan that I try to follow.**

Most of the time Christians say, "I'm praying for God to reveal His will for my life." That's one way to know God's will. Another way is to see where God is already working in the world, and jump in.

If a friend of yours asks why you seem so happy most of the time, that friend wants to know the reason you are happy. God is working on your friend. Pay attention, follow His will, and witness to your friend.

The Christian life is like an airplane flight from one side of the country to the other. You board the plane at the beginning of the trip (your Christian birth), and you deplane at the end of the trip (your death). You can either choose to stay inside the plane and continue flying the best, most direct route, or you can choose to get off at different stops. Some may offer pleasant, healthy attractions. Other stops may tempt you to do bad things. Sometimes it's a matter of choosing between something that is good for you and what is *best* for you.

Lynn Pryor, in his book *Get with God*, explains God's will this way:
- God's determined will is what He will do no matter what. For example, if God determines that people need to know who He is and Christians don't tell them, God will use other means.
- God's other will is His desired will. This is what He knows is best for us, but we still have choices.[1]

- **When you pray, "God, Your will be done" what do you think will happen?** _____
  _____
  _____

- **Does a prayer like that take the responsibility from you? Why or why not?** _____
  _____
  _____

- **How can you know what God's will is?** _____
  _____
  _____

**On the right side of the circle on page 10 write: Receiving, The Profits of Prayer, Acts 12:5,14.**

## NON-PROFIT PRAYERS

Rhoda and the Christians in Jerusalem prayed for Peter's release from prison. God answered their prayers by freeing Peter from prison. God answers all of your prayers. Sometimes, however, you may not like the answer. Other times, you may not recognize the answer. Occasionally, the answer takes a long time to come. Or, you may pray incorrectly.

- God will not answer unclear, non-specific prayers. How can He? If you can't state the specifics in prayer, you won't know God has answered. (For example, "Bless all the people in my school." What are their names?)

- God will not answer prayers that go against His natural will. (For example, if you love to drive fast, "God protect me" may not work.)

- God will not go against His personal nature. (For example, He will not cause evil to happen to someone because you want revenge.)

- God will not answer a prayer when you fail to do your part. (For example, praying to God is not going to give you an "A" in English if you never study.)

- God will not answer your prayer when you ask for something selfishly. (For example, God won't help you find a job if your motivation is to get lots of "stuff.")

To receive answers to your prayers keep these things in mind:
❑ Pray within God's will.
❑ Be specific in what you ask God to do.
❑ Do not pray for something that goes against God's nature.
❑ Be sure your reason for praying is pure and honorable.

**In the following case studies, teenagers like you wrestle with receiving answers to their prayers. Use the previous checklist to evaluate each and consider how you might respond.**

**Juanita's grandmother had been so lively until she fell and broke her hip. She was hospitalized, then developed pneumonia. Juanita's mother stayed at the hospital around the clock. Juanita continually asked God to heal her grandmother. She cried angry, bitter tears when her grandmother died.**

- **Why was Juanita's prayer not answered the way she wanted?** __
  _____
  _____
  _____

- **How could you comfort and encourage Juanita?** _____
  _____
  _____
  _____

Micah tried out for the varsity basketball team. He had played on the junior varsity team, but wanted to play on the varsity team so he would get more attention from others. "Please, God, help me make the team," Micah prayed the day of tryouts. Micah didn't make the team.

• Why was Micah's prayer not answered the way he wanted?

_____

_____

_____

• What might you say to Micah about not making the team?

_____

_____

Trey announced to the youth group that he believed God didn't exist. When asked why, he said, "He never answers my prayers." Trey explained that he had asked God to show him His will for his life, and he still didn't know what he was supposed to do in the future.

• What do you think about Trey's prayer? _____

_____

_____

• What might you say to help him receive an answer? _____

_____

_____

_____

REFLECT

• What have you learned about answered prayers?  _____

_____

_____

• How has this session changed the way you pray? _____

_____

_____

## REACT

- **Think about what God has given you. List blessings and answered prayers you have received from God. Include answers that didn't turn out exactly the way you asked.**
- **What can you say to friends who complain they don't feel God is listening when they pray?**

## REQUEST

**Dear God,**
**Thank you for answering my prayers so many times. Thank you for_____.**
**Thank You for showing me Your will about _____.**
**Thank You for teaching me how to pray.**
**In Jesus' holy name, I ask,**
**Amen.**

---

[1]Adapted from *Get with God*, Lynn H. Pryor (Nashville: Broadman and Holman Publishers, 1995), 80-81. Used by permission.

# The Pits
## The Pain of Prayer

**Y**ou can't live on the mountaintop of an emotionally intense relationship with God all the time. All Christians experience periods when life's crises crush the joy out of life —whether it's circumstances beyond your control or the consequences of your sin. Every mountain peak has a valley. In this session you'll look at those valleys and find out how to climb out of them.

**In the following "pitfalls" decide what is the "pit" (problem) and how the person might pray about the situation.**

**Pit 1—Kinsey did it on a dare. The others swore that the store owner had never caught them shoplifting. She got caught.**
**The Pit**_____
**A Prayer** _____

**Pit 2—Jamey's college education savings had to be used to pay the medical bills for his mother's illness. Jamey goes to a local college so he can live at home.**
**The Pit**_____
**A Prayer** _____

**Pit 3—Liza didn't think the lies she told about Jennie would end up getting Jennie in trouble at school.**
**The Pit**_____
**A Prayer** _____

**Pit 4—Ruthanne would give anything to relive that night. Now, she's pregnant.**

**The Pit** _____

**A Prayer** _____

**Pit 5—William's girlfriend of 18 months ended their relation-ship last night.**

**The Pit** _____

**A Prayer** _____

You'll study two kinds of pits in this study. One is the pit of difficult, painful circumstances that are sad, unavoidable parts of everyone's life. Prayer provides the hope needed to get through this time. Both the person who is affected by the situation and those who care about this person can pray for God's strength and support in times of difficulty.

The other pit involves the consequences of sin. This pit is the direct, or indirect, result of sin—yours or someone else's. This time the prayer might include confession of sin, repentance (turning away from the sin), and a desire to be forgiven by God.

The prayer of confession is painful. It's hard to admit personal sin. You can't just ask God to forgive all your sins. You must name your sin ("I intentionally hurt my mom's feelings"; "I got drunk and still drove home"; "I cheated on a math test"). God already knows your sin, but He wants to be sure that you recognize the sin in your life.

## A PAINFUL SITUATION

Stephen, a Christian chosen to be a deacon in the church in Jerusalem, was killed by the Jewish Sanhedrin. He was the first recorded Christian martyr. He was stoned outside the city wall of Jerusalem following a speech he made to the Sanhedrin. _Acts 6:8_ says that Stephen, _a man full of God's grace and power, did great wonders and miraculous signs among the people (Acts 6:8)._ Stephen must have been an amazing young man. First, he was chosen by the leadership of the Christian church in Jerusalem to serve with seven other men as deacons. They helped the disciples take care of the many people who were being converted daily to Christianity.

**Read about Stephen in *Acts 6:5*, then write two or three words or phrases that describe him.**_____

_____

_____

Because he spoke about his faith and healed many people, Stephen caught the attention of the Sanhedrin. They may have bribed several people to lie about Stephen when he was brought up for trial. When asked if the charges against him were true, Stephen spoke boldly about Jesus Christ. His sermon is recorded in *Acts-7:2-53*. In his closing words he condemned the Sanhedrin for killing Jesus and rejecting His teaching. That accusation angered the Sanhedrin. They drug Stephen out of the city and threw stones at him until he died. Read about Stephen's last prayer in *Acts 7:54-60*.

Death by stoning was cruel and painful. Yet, Stephen prayed with his dying breath for those who killed him. Stephen's prayer surely touched the life of another man, Paul (at that time called Saul). The influence of prayer spreads like the spark of a fire. Stephen caught the spark of eternal life from his personal relationship with Christ and passed it on. From Paul, it spread to men and women in every corner of the world. Stephen had no idea how significant his simple prayer for God to receive his spirit and forgive others was.

Have you ever wandered through a cemetery and read the epitaphs (final words) on the tombstones? Sometimes these reveal interesting information about the people buried beneath them. Here are a few real-life epitaphs, some of famous people.

Emily Dickinson
*CALLED BACK*

Lorenzo Sabine
*TRANSPLANTED*

Ellen Shannon
*Who was fatally burned March 21, 1870*
*by the explosion of a lamp filled with "R.E. Danforth's*
*Non-Explosive Burning Fluid"*

Sir Arthur Conan Doyle
*Steel True, Blade Straight*

Wyatt & Josephine Earp
*...that nothing's so sacred as honor and nothing's so loyal as love*

Oliver Hardy
*1892-1957*
*A GENIUS OF COMEDY*
*HIS TALENT BROUGHT JOY AND LAUGHTER TO ALL THE WORLD.*

**Based on the information you know about Stephen from the Scripture and his last prayer, write an epitaph for Stephen.**

_____

_____

_____

Do you remember the three parts of the "Prayer Circle" that you've added so far? See if these words help—centered, asking, receiving.

**At the bottom of the circle on page 10 write: The Pits, The Pain of Prayer, Acts 7:59-60.**

## A PAINFUL CONFESSION

This next story should be one of sin, confession, and forgiveness, but that's not what happened. The confession was too difficult to face; the results were deadly.

Ananias and his wife Sapphira, were members of the church in Jerusalem. Both collapsed and died immediately after Peter confronted them for lying about the profits on the property they sold. They kept some of the profit for themselves while pretending to give it all to the church.

They didn't have to give everything to the church. They could have said, "We sold some land, and we're giving half of the profits to the church." Instead, they implied (may have even bragged) about the fact that they were giving the total profits of the sale to the church. Peter said, "You have not lied to men but to God."

**Read the story about these two people in *Acts 5:1-10*. Write down the facts as you understand them.** _____

_____

_____

_____

_____

_____

_____

Instead of admitting they had lied and asking for forgiveness, Ananias and Sapphira continued to be devious. Was death too strong a punishment? Weren't they just disobedient? God saw the lie as a sin that corrupted their hearts. God didn't want anyone else to be corrupted by the sin of lying, cheating, or stealing.

**Two more tombstones to think about. What would you write for the epitaphs for Ananias and Sapphira?** _____

_____

_____

_____

_____

_____

_____

The story of Ananias and Sapphira is an example of how NOT to handle the pitfalls of life. Yes, it can be painful to admit sin. Yes, it can be painful to ask God for forgiveness. You might have to ask others for forgiveness, too. But, there is assurance that sins are forgiven when repentance is shown.

**Read *Acts 2:38* and *Acts 10:43*. Write a statement about confessing sin.** _____

_____

_____

_____

How does your statement relate to the statement next to "C" in the ACTS acronym? Confession is the "C" part of ACTS. So far you've studied the "S" and the "T" parts.

**Supply the missing letters and words.**

**Adoration**          **Praise God for who He is.**
**Confession**         **Admit your sins to God and ask His forgiveness.**
**T** _____      **Thank** _____.
**S** _____      **Ask** _____.

## PIT STOP

In auto racing the driver makes pit stops during the race to get the tires changed, to refuel, and to check out any problems. Pit crews are as important as the driver in winning the race. A slow pit crew can cause a highly qualified, skilled driver to lose the race.

When life gives us the pits of painful situations and the responsibility of living with the consequences of sin, that's the time to enlist a "prayer pit" crew. When you are in the middle of a mess, it's hard to know how to pray. That's when it's important to have friends who will pray for you. You will never know the true value of friends until they stand beside you in tough times and pray for you.

**Write the names of several friends who might be willing to be your pit crew (prayer partners). These could be persons attending this study.**

**Crew Member** _____ **Phone or e-mail** _____
**Crew Member** _____ **Phone or e-mail** _____
**Crew Member** _____ **Phone or e-mail** _____
**Crew Member** _____ **Phone or e-mail** _____
**Crew Member** _____ **Phone or e-mail** _____

Refueling is a key reason for making a pit stop. Prayer fuels your life. When you pray, confessing your sin and asking for forgiveness, it's like getting a fresh start with a full tank of gas.

When you became a Christian, God made you a brand-new being. By confessing sin, even when it's painful, you keep that God-changed new being clean and pure. Confession does not remove the consequences; God won't make those disappear. However, God walks with you and helps you survive the consequences.

**What are some ways you can refuel your life through prayer? (A couple are listed to get you started.)**

**Be honest with myself and God**

**Talk to God regularly**

_____

_____

_____

### REFLECT

• **Write sins that you need to confess to God. You can write abbreviations or just one word that reminds you of this sin.**

_____

_____

_____

_____

_____

• **Thinking back over this study, how do you feel about these sins?** _____

_____

_____

• **What are you willing to do about these sins?** _____

_____

_____

• **Reflect back on the painful circumstances in your life, especially current situations. Write down two or three words that express the emotions and pain you have about these.** _____

_____

_____

### REACT

**Stephen had a steady faith. He trusted God to lead him through death to eternal life in the same way that he trusted God to lead him through his daily life. His testimony changed others, even after his death.**

• How clear and convincing is the testimony you offer to the world? _____

_____

_____

• Think of a person you know who does not know Christ as Savior. How could you witness to this person about who Christ is and what He means to you? _____

_____

_____

• Think of ways your influence can help a Christian friend grow spiritually. List several of those ways here. _____

_____

_____

## REQUEST

In previous sessions, this request has taken the form of a guided prayer. This time you can use this space to write either a prayer of confession and repentance, or a prayer over a painful situation in your life that really needs God's help. _____

_____

_____

_____

_____

_____

_____

_____

# The Pinnacle
## The Praise of Prayer

I f you attend the worship service at your church, you may sing praise choruses. Some churches sing the "Doxology" which is defined as a way to praise God. Worship praises God. Praise is verbal applause.

**The early Christians spent their time in Christian fellowship and praising God. Read *Acts 2:46-47*. What happened when they praised God?** _____
_____
_____

Praise is the "A" part of ACTS. We have to use "A" for adoration. There's no "P" in ACTS for praise.

**Supply the missing letters and words.**

| Adoration | Praise God for who He is. |
|-----------|---------------------------|
| C _____ | Admit _____. |
| T _____ | Thank _____. |
| S _____ | Ask _____. |

### "FATHER, I ADORE YOU"

Adoration expresses love, joy, pleasure, awe, acceptance, and worship. When directed to God, adoration praises the nature of God, His characteristics, His being. Adoration differs from thanksgiving. Thanksgiving thanks God for His blessings, His answers to our prayers, His comfort and care of us. Thanksgiving deals with actions; adoration deals with being. Thanksgiving thanks God for what He does; adoration thanks God for who He is.

**Circle the titles that adore or praise God.**

| | | |
|---|---|---|
| Father | Spirit | Brother |
| Physician | Rabbi | Messiah |
| Almighty | Holy | Savior |
| I Am | Prophet | Faithful |
| Perfect | Loving | Shepherd |
| Creator | Majesty | Just |
| Infinite | Powerful | Peace |
| Wise | Refuge | Gracious |
| All-Knowing | Unique | King of kings |
| Unchangeable | Strength | Bride of Christ |

The only words that don't apply directly to God are rabbi, physician, brother, Savior, Prophet, Messiah, King of kings, and bride of Christ. These terms relate to Jesus. (You could circle King of kings, but it is a phrase usually given to Jesus.) The bride of Christ identifies the church's relationship to Jesus.

• **Why do I need to praise God? Doesn't He know He is great?**

_____

_____

• **What are some ways I can praise God in my life?** _____

_____

_____

• **How does saying a bunch of adjectives praise God?** _____

_____

_____

## PRAISING GOD FROM THE BEGINNING TO INFINITY

Acts is a history book that tells how the church began. It relates many stories, healings, and sermons of the first leaders of the Christian church. Chapters 1-12 tell about the work of Jesus' disciples in and around Jerusalem where the first Christian church was formed.

Chapters 14-28 describe Paul's missionary journeys. Chapter 13 reports how Paul was sent out to tell the rest of the world beyond Jerusalem about the good news of Jesus Christ. In it we find a powerful sermon that Paul preached to the people of Pisidian Antioch.

Have you ever heard history described as "His Story"? In his sermon Paul clearly revealed how God worked through the history of the Jewish people to save the world.

**Read *Acts 13:16–41*. Draw a time line of events that record God's actions in history.**

**• What did you learn about God from this time line?** _____

_____

_____

**• What words of praise that you circled earlier relate to the events of this time line?** _____

_____

_____

### PRAYING IN PRAISE

A key characteristic of God is His loving nature. That means God loves you. God loves unconditionally.

**Check the statements that complete the sentence and explain unconditional love. God loves me . . .**
❏ **even when I say His name in cursing.**
❏ **only when I remember to praise Him.**
❏ **even when I lie to my mother or father.**
❏ **only when I think good, pure thoughts.**
❏ **even when I forget to spend time alone with Him.**

If you chose the first, third, and fifth statements you understand unconditional love. This love is not based on a person's actions, but on the fact that God created you. Your actions may damage your relationship with God, but He will still love you. Some religions require you to work your way into their heavens through good deeds. But not Christianity. God says, "I will love you no matter what, because my nature is love."

To return God's love you can praise Him in prayer. As you communicate your love to God, you learn to love. Have you ever written or emailed a person you love? Prayer is a way to express your feelings of love to God. It gets your mouth and heart working together. Praying in praise lets the mouth say what the heart feels.

**Write a love letter to God. Describe your appreciation and affection for Him. (If you struggle with putting your praise into writing, pretend you are talking to a family member, friend, teacher, or coach about your appreciation for him or her. What would you say?)**_____

_____

_____

_____

_____

_____

## PUTTING PRAYER INTO PRACTICE

In these five sessions you've learned some important things about prayer. You've seen that:

- you can pray because Jesus told us to pray, and His name makes our prayers acceptable to God;
- in prayer you can ask anything that is within God's will, and He will answer your prayers;
- receiving answers to your prayers comes in different ways;
- prayer supports you through the difficult circumstances of life;
- prayer is the way to confess your sins to God;
- God is worthy of your prayers of praise because of who He is.

Now, it's time to put these ideas about prayer into practice. Start with your world. In session 2 you filled in a chart that listed places in your world with people who had needs. Have you been praying for these people? Don't walk away from this study with nice thoughts about prayer that you never put into action.

**The followers of Jesus started in Jerusalem and then spread their message. Using *Acts 1:8* as a model, write in the names of people in each of these areas. Ask God to bring to mind the people to include.**

**My Home (Jerusalem)**

_____

_____

_____

_____

**My Neighborhood (Judea)**

_____

_____

_____

_____

**My School (Samaria)**

_____

_____

_____

_____

**My Job, Team, Other Friends (the ends of the earth)**

_____

_____

_____

_____

Are you memorizing the parts of the "Prayer Circle?" Now is a good time. We're going to add several things to the circle.

**At the top of the circle on page 10 write: The Pinnacle, The Praise of Prayer, *Acts 2:46–47*.**

**Inside the circle write the names of Christian friends and family members.**

**Outside the circle write the names of friends, family, neighbors, fellow employees, and others who are unsaved.**

• **What will it take to move the names of the people from the outside of the circle into the circle?** _____
_____
_____

• **How can these people on the outside of the circle know about Jesus Christ?** _____
_____
_____

• **What part are you willing to play in helping these people understand who Jesus is and how He can change their lives?** _
_____
_____

• **Write the names of two people who are outside the circle that you will pray for every day for the next few weeks. Ask God to show you how to share Jesus with them.**
   1. _____
   2. _____

In session 4 you identified pit crew members (prayer partners). One way to continue to grow in your prayer life is to be accountable to other people. Ask the people whose names you listed to be your prayer supporters. Encourage one another to keep a regular time alone with God. You can call on one another when you have a prayer request or when you need prayer reinforcement.

In addition to those you listed who might be attending this study, consider adding someone from your family. You might want to add a Christian friend from school or at work who can hold you accountable. The purpose is to help both of you remember to stay in touch with God through regular prayer.

Put this commitment in writing by completing and signing the Prayer Life Covenant on page 62. Ask two other people to sign as your witnesses. There are places for you to add your own ideas about the covenant. This way you can make your covenant personal.

## REFLECT

• **What do you want to remember about this session?** _____

_____

_____

• **What do you want to remember about this study on prayer?**

_____

_____

• **What surprised you most about this study on prayer?** _____

_____

_____

• **What encouraged you the most about this study on prayer?** _

_____

_____

## REACT

• **As a result of this study what one thing can you do immediately to improve your prayer life?** _____

_____

_____

_____

• **What will it take to make this happen for you?** _____

_____

_____

_____

**Someone has said, "Don't seek God's hand, until you seek His face." What do you think that means?** _____

_____

_____

**Write a prayer that seeks God's face.** _____

_____

_____

# Group Learning Activities

**C**ircle Your World with Prayer focuses on helping students experience prayer in a fresh and meaningful way. The content and interactive nature makes this study ideal for a DiscipleNow. The five sessions can also be easily adapted to fit a retreat setting.

You may find it helpful to divide into age groups in order to increase the effectiveness of these activities aimed at developing a sense of closeness with God and His family.

You will find an illustration of the completed Prayer Circle on page 61 to help your students in completing their assignments each session.

Attached to the back cover is a My Prayer Circle Bookmark for students to detach as a reminder and source of encouragement.

# **Prayer**
# Centered in Jesus

**Things You Need to Get**
Pencils
Paper
Ten half sheets of construction paper
Marker
Three-by-five inch cards
Copy of *Circle Your World With Prayer* for each student
Candy (optional)

**Things You Need to Do**
In large letters, on each half sheet of construction paper, list one of the 10 events in Jesus' life from "Previously on Planet Earth . . ." (p. 5).

Be prepared to explain the Prayer Circle diagram on page 10.

## 1. ELECTRICITY (10 MINUTES)

Have students stand in a circle. Explain how to play Electricity. One person squeezes the hand of the person on the right, who passes on the squeeze until it has been around the circle. After one practice round, get someone with a watch to time how fast the squeeze can go around the circle. As a variation, call "Switch" at any time. If the squeeze was going around to those on the right, after "switch" the squeeze goes to the left.

## 2. THE CIRCLE THEME (5 MINUTES)

Use the Introduction on page 4 to explain the theme of *Circle Your World With Prayer*. Divide students into teams of no more than five. Give each team a sheet of paper and a pencil. Tell teams they have 90 seconds to list things that go in a circle or that are circular. After 90 seconds, call time. Let teams share. (*Option: Award candy to the winning team.*)

### 3. THE REASON FOR PRAYER (10 MINUTES)

Hand out *Circle Your World With Prayer* books and pencils. Explain that a circle is the first focus of the theme for this study. The circle safely holds everything within it; for this study that involves the world of the students which is the second focus. The third focus of the study is prayer. Ask: **Why do we pray? How does prayer happen?** If no one mentions Jesus as the reason we can pray to God, ask, **What part does Jesus play in prayer?**

Point out "Previously on Planet Earth. . ." (p. 5). Place the half sheets of construction paper containing each event on the floor, directing youth to arrange them in chronological order. *(Using first words, the correct order is: born, grew, traveled, taught, accused, died, buried, mysteriously, seen, ascended.)* Direct students to "What Does Jesus Have to Do With Prayer?" (p. 5). Assign each statement about Jesus and the related question to pairs of students to discuss and present to the larger group.

### 4. THE DEFINITION OF PRAYER (10 MINUTES)

Direct students to "What's Prayer All About?" (p. 6). Have students choose the best definition of prayer. Let volunteers share and defend their choices. Assign each of the eight Scriptures from Acts to one or two students. Tell students to complete the chart, deciding which prayer definition fits their assigned Scripture. Call for responses. Emphasize how vital prayer was to the new Christian movement.

### 5. THE WEEK THAT WAS (10 MINUTES)

Say, **Let's take a look at how vital prayer is today.** Direct students to complete the chart under "The Week That Was" (p. 8) marking on the chart a dot for their life and a cross for their prayer life. Invite volunteers to share. Discuss questions on pages 8-9. Encourage students to select one word that best summarizes their week, using the suggested words.

### 6. THE CENTER OF PRAYER (10 MINUTES)

Ask the opening questions in "The Center of Prayer" (p. 9). Ask a student to read *Acts 2:36*. Explain the importance of Jesus being called Lord and Christ. Direct students to the "Prayer Circle" on page 10. Explain how to mark the center, as suggested. See page 61 for an illustration of the completed Prayer Circle.

Hand out the three-by-five inch cards, stating that during this study you want to pray for them. Direct students to write their names at the top of the card and then a prayer concern. Collect the cards. Before the last session take time to write a verse about prayer that relates to the concern on each card. You will return cards to the students during the last session.

## 7. PRAYING (5 MINUTES)

If you are meeting on a clear evening go outside. Ask, **How does it feel being out here on a planet that is just a small part of a huge universe?** Pause, then say: **You are significant because of Jesus Christ. When you pray you are, in effect, standing before God.**

Direct students to hold hands. Share that it is not necessary to close our eyes when we pray, but doing so helps us concentrate better. Lead students in a time of prayer. *(Option: Direct students to individually complete "Reflect," "React," and "Request" on pages 11-12.)*

# **Asking**
# The Power of Prayer

## Session 2

**Things You Need to Get**
Large sheets of paper
Markers
Colored beads (or small pebbles)
Colored construction paper
Scissors

**Things You Need to Do**
Using the colored construction paper, cut out the letters A, C, T, S. You will use these in the remaining sessions.

### 1. THE PROMISE (15 MINUTES)
Depending on the size of your group, form one or more circles of six to eight people. Stand shoulder to shoulder, facing the center with hands held at chest height. Ask a volunteer to stand in the center of the circle with feet together, arms crossed over chest, and eyes closed. Tell the student in the center to keep his body stiff and lean back, letting the people in the circle gently push him around the circle. Direct those standing in the circle to support the center person with their hands, with at least two people supporting the person at all times. Assure the volunteer, "We'll catch you, I promise." Say this several times. Repeat the activity with different students in the center. Assure these volunteers too.

Ask: **Why did you trust these people to keep you from falling? Did anyone make a promise to you? Why did you believe the promise? When is a promise not a promise?**

Turn to session 2 (p. 13) and respond to the six questions. Then have students turn to *Acts 1:4* and *Acts 2:1-4* in their Bibles. Read the Scripture and complete the activities under "The Promise" (p. 14). Ask, **How are promises related to prayers?**

## 2. THE POWER OF PRAYER (15 MINUTES)

Examine how prayer and the Holy Spirit changed the lives of the disciples, using Peter as an example. Divide students into two teams. Direct **Team 1** to "The Power of Prayer" (p. 15). **Team 1** will check out Peter before he received the Holy Spirit by reading the Scripture and preparing the "Peter" acrostic. **Team 2** will check out Peter after receiving the Holy Spirit by reading that Scripture and preparing the "Power" acrostic. Give each team a large sheet of paper and a marker for the acrostic. Call for team reports. Remind students how they can receive the same power. Offer to talk individually to those who have not made professions of faith.

Place the four letters of ACTS on the floor. Explain how ACTS is an acronym to remember four ways to pray. Point out these ways under "Asking in Prayer" (p. 16). Say: **In this session we will look at supplication. Supplication is the "asking" part of prayer.**

## 3. THE PEOPLE OF PRAYER (15 MINUTES)

State that it's OK to ask God for something in prayer, but the request has to be worthy and appropriate. Using the same two teams, direct **Team 1** to examine "Asking for the Right Thing"(p. 16) and **Team 2** to examine "Asking for the Wrong Thing" (p. 17). Direct teams to prepare skits (using everyone on their team) that share their assigned story. When teams are ready, call for the skits.

## 4. ASKING FOR OTHERS (10 MINUTES)

Explain the meaning of intercession. Direct students to add the "Asking" section to the left of the circle (p. 10) as instructed on page 18.

Lead youth to brainstorm places that are a part of their world (home, school, church, team, neighborhood, job, etc.). Write these on a large sheet of paper with a marker. Direct students to the "My World" chart (p. 19). Tell students to select three places in their world and write them on their chart. Then have students to write the names and needs on the chart.

Pass out colored beads (or small pebbles), telling students to take three of different colors, if possible. Say: **Assign each bead (pebble) to represent one person on your list. Sometimes we get so focused on our own problems that it's hard to remember to pray for others. Place the beads (pebbles) in your pocket. Carry them at least as long as this study lasts. Let them remind you to pray for these people each time you reach into your pocket. When your prayer is answered, throw away the bead (pebble) or give it to the person you've prayed for.**

### 5. ASKING FOR YOURSELF (5 MINUTES)

Ask students to form prayer groups of three to six. Stand in a circle and hold hands. Say: **We've talked about praying for others. Silently pray for the person on your right** (pause) **and the person on your left** (pause). **Pray for yourself. Reflect on a need or problem you have. If you feel comfortable, share your need with the others and let them pray for you. If no one talks, that's OK, too**.

After a few minutes, softly begin to sing the chorus "God Is So Good," or another song. Encourage students to join in. *(Option: Direct students to individually complete "Reflect," "React," and "Request" on page 20.)*

# **Receiving:**
# The Profits of Prayer

## Session 3

**Things You Need to Get**
Quiet contemporary Christian music
Tape player or CD player
Blindfolds for step 1 (optional)
ACTS letters from session 2
Pencils

### 1. BLESSINGS (10 MINUTES)

Divide students into two teams. Direct the members of **Team 1** to sit in different locations throughout the room and close their eyes as they wait to receive a blessing from **Team 2**. *(Option: If you work with younger students use blindfolds to help them remain quiet.)* Explain to **Team 2** that when the music starts they will give blessings to members of **Team 1**. State that the blessing could be a pat on the back, a hug, a hand on the shoulder. Students do not have to form a line or go in any specific order. They should, however, bless everyone on **Team 1**. Do this in silence. Play contemporary Christian music during this time. After everyone on **Team 1** has been blessed, reverse the process.

After both teams have received blessings, ask: **Was it more comfortable to receive or to give the blessing? Why? When you were receiving the blessings, how did you feel? When you were giving the blessings, how did you feel? How did keeping your eyes closed affect the experience?** *(Option: If your group is too active for this opening activity, direct students to the "Would you ..." questions on page 21.)*

Share that the group will study the receiving part of prayer. Place the large letters of ACTS on the floor. Ask: **Which letter did we study in the last session?** *("S" for supplication)* **What did it mean?** *(Ask for God's* *help.*) Explain that in this session students will study "T." Let them look at "Praying for Profit" (p. 21) to discover what "T" stands for.

## 2. SURPRISE! ANSWERED PRAYER (20 MINUTES)

Have students turn to "Excuse Me–Didn't you Forget Something?" (p. 22). Hand out pencils and tell them to work in pairs to find and circle the 13 mistakes in the story about Rhoda. Next, direct them to *Acts 12:1-17* to check their circled mistakes, writing in the correct information. After a few minutes review the story. (*Mistakes and answers are: Augustus–Herod; feed–kill; Paul–Peter; Pentecost–Unleavened Bread; hunger–safety; pillars–guards; guard dogs–guards; blind–on the side; ankles–wrists; pagans–Christians; rang the doorbell–knocked; climbed the wall–knocked again; the kitchen–prison.*) Ask the questions following the story on pages 23-24.

## 3. PRAYER CIRCLE AND PROFITS (10 MINUTES)

Examine what it means to receive in prayer from God, by directing students to select a definition of the will of God from those listed on page 24. Briefly summarize the information found in the section "Praying in God's Will."

To help them understand the variety of blessings they can receive from praying, direct students to "Plenty of Profits" (p. 22). Have them circle blessings they have experienced as a result of praying. Invite students to share times when prayer was answered. Ask, **What blessings did you receive from the experience?**

Direct students to add the "Receiving" section to the right of the circle (p. 10) as instructed on page 25.

## 4. NON-PROFIT PRAYERS (15 MINUTES)

Acknowledge that sometimes it seems like God does not answer prayers. Divide into three teams, assigning each team a case study from pages 26-27. Point out the four check box statements (p. 26) that can be used to evaluate each situation. After a few minutes ask teams to read their case studies and answers the questions. (*Option: If your students like drama, let teams prepare skits about their case study.*

## 5. THE CIRCLE IN MOTION (5 MINUTES)

Ask students to join hands and stand in a circle. Stand between two of the students and gently "break" the circle. Take the hand of only one of the students and begin spiraling toward the remaining students (The group will resemble a human cinnamon roll). Daw everyone into a tight coil wrapped around one another.

Share that as believers we are one body in Christ. Lead students to repeat the Lord's Prayer. Sing a familiar chorus. Close with a prayer thanking God for all His blessings. To unroll the spiral and avoid confusion, begin with the students on the outside. The rest should follow. *(Option: Direct students to individually complete "Reflect," "React," and "Request" on pages 27-28.)*

# The Pits
# The Pain of Prayer

**Things You Need to Get**
Large blanket
ACTS letters from session 2
Paper
Pencils

## 1. FROZEN PORTRAITS (10 MINUTES)

Divide students into two teams. Enlist two people to hold a blanket up as a divider between the two teams. Direct **Team 1** to arrange themselves into a "family portrait," arranging their bodies in creative ways. When **Team 1** is ready, drop the blanket or sheet and give the other team one minute to study the family portrait. Hold up the blanket again. Tell **Team 2** to duplicate the arrangement of **Team 1**. Drop the blanket and compare the two portraits. Then let **Team 1** copy the family portrait of **Team 2**. Say: **Behind the smiling faces of a family portrait people may be hurting physically or emotionally. They may be caught up in sin and not know how to stop. Today we look beyond the surface of the Christian church in Jerusalem to see the painful circumstances and sins in their family portrait.**

## 2. PITFALLS (10 MINUTES)

Assign each student (or pair of students) one of the "pits" on pages 29-30. Tell each student to explain the problem and then share a prayer that person might pray. Say: **The pain of prayer happens in two ways. One way occurs when prayer helps a person get through a painful situation, like a parent's illness or a broken relationship. Another way pain and prayer collide involves the painful confession of sin, like having sex outside of marriage or gossiping.**

## 3. SITUATIONS AND CONFESSIONS (20 MINUTES)

Using the original teams, assign **Team 1** to review "A Painful Situation" (p. 30) and **Team 2** to review "A Painful Confession" (p. 32). Have each team complete the epitaphs on the tombstones. In addition direct teams to either write an obituary of their person's death, a modern-day version of the story, or a rap telling the story. Have **Team 1** share their presentation about Stephen.

Direct students to add the "Pits" section at the bottom of the circle (p. 10) as instructed on page 32.

Have **Team 2** share their presentation about Ananias and Sapphira.

Place the ACTS letters on the floor. Challenge students to name what the "T" and "S" represent. *("T" is for thanksgiving. "S" is for supplication.)* Discuss the meaning of the words. *(Thanksgiving means to thank God for all He has done. Supplication means to ask for God's help.)* Explain that "C" is for confession.

## 4. PLANNING YOUR PIT CREW (10 MINUTES)

Say: **Like the family portrait activity at the beginning, we walk around looking OK on the outside, but inside we may be in the pits. Maybe it's a situation that's not your fault, but you're hurting over it. Maybe it's the consequences of a sin that you have confessed, but still must live with the consequences. Or maybe it's a sin that you're not willing to confess. Everyone has days that are the pits—even Christians.**

Direct students to turn to the inside front cover of this book. Ask them to write the epitaph for their personal tombstone. Explain that students will not be sharing these with the others.

Explain the importance of a pit crew, using the information on page 34. Encourage students to consider how other students in this study can be a part of their pit crew. Allow time to fill in the names and information about possible "crew members."

## 5. TESTIMONIES (10 MINUTES)

Share a time when you faced a difficult situation or dealt with a sin in your life. State how prayer helped you through the experience. Invite volunteers to share similar experiences.

Form one group circle or two team circles. Ask students to reflect on the personal epitaph they worked on. Say: **Let's begin this prayer time with everybody saying at once, "Lord, this is . . ." and add your name.** (Pause to do this.) **Silently confess in your mind and heart something that is bothering you. Ask for God's forgiveness. Ask Him to help you with a tough situation. If there is a part of your prayer that you wish to verbalize, begin it with the phrase "Lord, help me. . . ."** Wait quietly in the circle for others to speak if they choose. Close the prayer time.

*(Option: Direct students to individually complete "Reflect," "React," and "Request" on pages 35-36.)*

# The Pinnacle
# The Praise of Prayer

## Session 5

**Things You Need to Get**
ACTS letters from session 2
Large sheets of paper
Markers
Candy (optional)

**Things You Need to Do**
Plan a route for the prayer walk.
Three-by-five inch prayer cards from session 1.

### 1. LOVING GOD (15 MINUTES)

Place the ACTS letters on the floor. Challenge students to name what the "C", "T" and "S" represent. *("C" is for confession. "T" is for thanksgiving. "S" is for supplication.)* Discuss the meaning of the words. *(Confession means to admit your sins to God and ask for His forgiveness. Thanksgiving means to thank God for all He has done. Supplication means to ask for God's help.)* Explain that "A" stands for Adoration. Ask, **What does adoration mean?** Explain the difference between *adoring* God for who He is and *thanking* God for what He does.

Divide into two teams. Give each team a large sheet of paper and a marker. Tell teams they have two minutes to list characteristics and names of God. Don't let them use their books, but suggest they use their Bibles. The team with the longest list wins. Let each team share. Point out the names and characteristics of God on page 38. Direct students to find the words that don't relate to God. Discuss the questions that follow. *(Option: Award candy to the winning team.)*

Say: **Prayer is a language of love. A major trait of God is His unconditional love.** Ask, **What is unconditional love?** Direct students to choose an explanation of unconditional love from the statements under "Praying in Praise" (p. 39). Explain how prayer that praises God is a love letter to Him. Invite students to write a love letter to God in the space provided on page 40. Share letters.

## 2. PRAISING GOD (15 MINUTES)

Direct students to "Praising God from the Beginning to Infinity" (p. 38). Ask a student to read *Acts 13:16-41* aloud. Explain the background. Using the same two teams, tell students to turn over their sheets of paper and draw a time line of God's history with the Jews. Refer to the verses to get the information. Discuss the questions at the end of this section. Say: **Before God sent Jesus, He tried other ways to reach the Hebrew people, but they refused to follow Him. Sending Jesus was God's last hope of reaching those He loved. The Jews had many reasons to praise God, but they didn't.**

## 3. THE PRACTICAL SIDE OF PRAYER (30 MINUTES)

Help students understand how to put what they learned about prayer into practice. Ask, **What have you learned about prayer?** Say: **Prayer is vital for Christian growth. It gives Christians a way to talk to God about life.** Direct a student to read *Acts 1:8*. Point out the ever-expanding world for which students can pray.

If possible, conduct a prayer walk. If you are meeting in a home, ask the host if you can walk through several rooms of the house. Tell students to bring their books and pencils. As you stand in different rooms, ask, **Who does this room remind you of in your home?** (*For example, the kitchen may remind them of their moms.*) Tell students to write these names in their books on page 41. Walk outside, and through the neighborhood, if possible. Ask, **Who lives on either side of you in your neighborhood?** If you are close to a school, community center, or church, you might walk there and continue the experience. If not, find a place to sit outside, under a light if needed, as students work through this section. Remind students that their list represents actual people for whom they can pray.

Direct students to add the "Pinnacle" section at the top of the circle (p. 10) as instructed on page 41.

Conclude the prayer walk by encouraging students to make a commitment to pray regularly. Point out the "Prayer Life Covenant" (p. 62). Explain that this is voluntary. Stress the value of accountability. Ask students to sit alone to consider the covenant.

## 4. COMMISSIONED (15 MINUTES)

Call students together. Read *Acts 13:3* aloud. Say: **This is how the church at Antioch commissioned and sent out the first missionaries, Paul and Barnabas. You are returning to your world, hopefully a changed person. We are commissioning you to return to your world as one who will pray for your world, for the people in your world, and for yourself.**

You can conduct the commissioning service in one of several ways: (1) Pray one prayer for all students at the same time. (2) Place your hands on each student's head, saying a brief prayer for each student one at a time. (3) Divide into two teams. Have a student on each team to kneel in the center while the others place their hands on him or her. Have one person pray. Continue until everyone has been prayed for.

Return the three-by-five inch prayer cards from session 1 on which you have written a verse about prayer that relates to the concern on each card. *(Option: Direct youth to individually complete "Reflect," "React," and "Request" on pages 43-44.)*

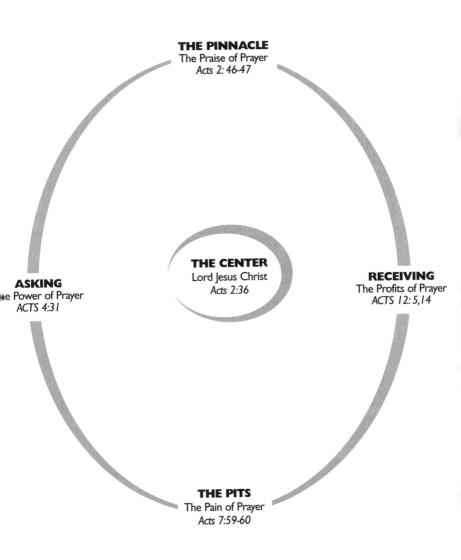

**THE PINNACLE**
The Praise of Prayer
Acts 2: 46-47

**ASKING**
e Power of Prayer
ACTS 4:31

**THE CENTER**
Lord Jesus Christ
Acts 2:36

**RECEIVING**
The Profits of Prayer
ACTS 12: 5,14

**THE PITS**
The Pain of Prayer
Acts 7:59-60

# Prayer Life Covenant

I, _____, promise to pray at least ❑ once ❑ twice ❑ three or ❑ more times a day / week. In my prayers I will:

❑ **(Adoration) Praise God for who He is.**
❑ **(Confession) Tell my sins to God and ask for His forgiveness.**
❑ **(Thanksgiving) Thank God for His many blessings to me.**
❑ **(Supplication) Ask God to help me and others.**

I realize that I cannot pray in my own power, so I ask God to use His Holy Spirit in my life to help me pray faithfully.

In addition, I want to add (write your own thoughts about your prayer life) _____
_____
_____
_____

Signed (your name) _____
Witnessed by _____
Witnessed by _____
On (today's date): _____

# CHRISTIAN GROWTH STUDY PLAN

## Preparing Christians to Serve

In the Christian Growth Study Plan, this book *Circle Your World with Prayer* is a resource for course credit in the subject area Prayer-Youth. To receive credit, read the book, complete the learning activities, show your work to your pastor, youth minister, or church leader; then complete the information on the next page. The form may be duplicated. Send the completed page to:

**Christian Growth Study Plan**
**127 Ninth Avenue, North, MSN 117**
**Nashville, TN 37234-0117**
**FAX: (615)251-5067**

For more information about the Christian Growth Study Plan, refer to the current *Christian Growth Study Plan Catalog*. Your church office may have a copy. If not, request a free copy from the Christian Growth Study Plan office, phone 615-251-2525, or fax 615-251-5067.

Circle Your Word With Prayer

# COURSE NUMBER: CG-0492

Rev. 6-99

## PARTICIPANT INFORMATION

| Social Security Number (USA Only) | Personal CGSP Number* | | Date of Birth (Mo., Day, Yr.) |
|---|---|---|---|
| — — | — | — | — — |

Name (First, MI, Last)

Address (Street, Route, or P.O. Box)

City, State, or Province

Home Phone —

Zip/Postal Code

## CHURCH INFORMATION

Church Name

Address (Street, Route, or P.O. Box)

City, State, or Province

Zip/Postal Code

## CHANGE REQUEST ONLY

☐Former Name

☐Former Address

City, State, or Province

Zip/Postal Code

☐Former Church

City, State, or Province

Zip/Postal Code

Signature of Pastor, Conference Leader, or Other Church Leader

Date

*New participants are requested but not required to give SS# and date of birth. Existing participants, please give CGSP# when using SS# for the first time.

Thereafter, only one ID# is required. *Mail To:* Christian Growth Study Plan, 127 Ninth Ave., North, MSN 117, Nashville, TN 37234-0117. Fax:
(615)251-5067